To My Dear Heart: _____

From: _____

Date: _____

Rise and Shine
Dear Heart

Written by Jessica Ann Mitchell Aiwuyor

Our Legaci Press, LLC

Rise and Shine, Dear Heart

First Printing, 2018

ISBN 978-1-948061-02-5

Our Legaci Press, LLC
P.O. Box 471221
6514 Marlboro Pike
District Heights, MD 20747

www.OurLegaciPress.com

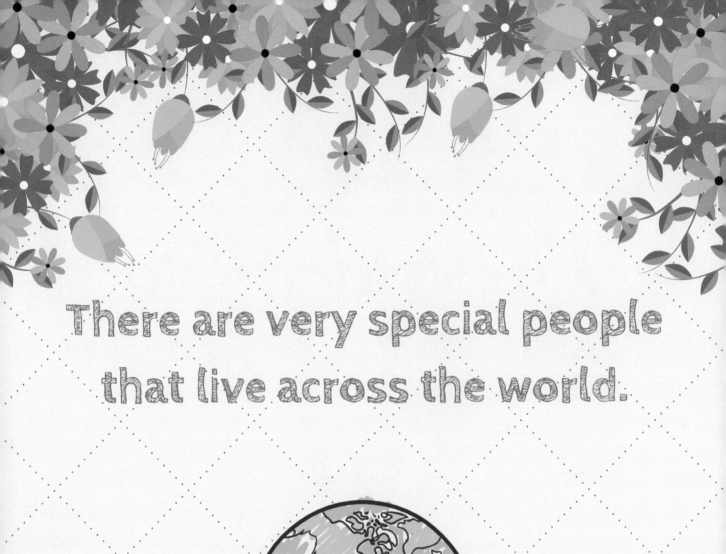

There are very special people that live across the world.

They have many different gifts.
They are brilliant little girls.

We call them our dear hearts
because we love them so.

Right now, they're very young
but someday they'll surely grow.

You are my
own dear heart.
I love you
through and through.

While you're
still my little one,
here's a
special poem
for you.

Rise and Shine!

Go ahead and be yourself.

Free. Free. Free.

To tell your story.
To sing your song.

Explore the world.

Take care of yourself.

Laugh with your friends.

Rise and shine,
dear heart.

Go ahead and...

Do your dance.

Try new things.

And follow your dreams.

Most of all,
dear heart...

Love who you are and
you will go far.

You rise like the sun.
You shine like a jewel.

You glow like three moons.
You're a flower in bloom.

If you're ever feeling sad or blue, just remember this is true.

You are
a precious
work of art.
You are super
important and
really smart.

One day,
you can
go real high.

One day,
you can
touch the sky.

If you
reach for the
stars,
you may
land
on the
moon.

But you'll never know, if you give up too soon.

Just keep going.
Just keep trying.

Just keep rising.
Just keep shining.

Remember
this every single
day.
You are
gifted in your own
special way.

And you will always be my
dear heart.

CPSIA information can be obtained
at www.ICGtesting.com
Printed in the USA
BVHW020414070421
604335BV00015B/388